# Flowers in Bloom

## THIS BOOK BELONGS TO

_____

ADDRESS

_____

_____

_____

_____

TELEPHONE

_____

| | |
|---|---|
| NAME | NAME |
| ADDRESS | ADDRESS |
| | |
| | |
| TELEPHONE | TELEPHONE |
| MOBILE | MOBILE |
| E-MAIL | E-MAIL |
| | |
| NAME | NAME |
| ADDRESS | ADDRESS |
| | |
| | |
| TELEPHONE | TELEPHONE |
| MOBILE | MOBILE |
| E-MAIL | E-MAIL |
| | |
| NAME | NAME |
| ADDRESS | ADDRESS |
| | |
| | |
| TELEPHONE | TELEPHONE |
| MOBILE | MOBILE |
| E-MAIL | E-MAIL |

| NAME | NAME |
|---|---|
| ADDRESS | ADDRESS |
| | |
| | |
| TELEPHONE | TELEPHONE |
| MOBILE | MOBILE |
| E-MAIL | E-MAIL |
| | |
| NAME | NAME |
| ADDRESS | ADDRESS |
| | |
| | |
| TELEPHONE | TELEPHONE |
| MOBILE | MOBILE |
| E-MAIL | E-MAIL |
| | |
| NAME | NAME |
| ADDRESS | ADDRESS |
| | |
| | |
| TELEPHONE | TELEPHONE |
| MOBILE | MOBILE |
| E-MAIL | E-MAIL |

NAME

ADDRESS


TELEPHONE

MOBILE

E-MAIL


NAME

ADDRESS


TELEPHONE

MOBILE

E-MAIL


NAME

ADDRESS


TELEPHONE

MOBILE

E-MAIL

NAME

ADDRESS


TELEPHONE

MOBILE

E-MAIL


NAME

ADDRESS


TELEPHONE

MOBILE

E-MAIL


NAME

ADDRESS


TELEPHONE

MOBILE

E-MAIL

NAME

ADDRESS

TELEPHONE

MOBILE

E-MAIL

NAME

ADDRESS

TELEPHONE

MOBILE

E-MAIL

NAME

ADDRESS

TELEPHONE

MOBILE

E-MAIL

NAME

ADDRESS

TELEPHONE

MOBILE

E-MAIL

NAME

ADDRESS

TELEPHONE

MOBILE

E-MAIL

NAME

ADDRESS

TELEPHONE

MOBILE

E-MAIL

NAME

ADDRESS


TELEPHONE

MOBILE

E-MAIL


NAME

ADDRESS


TELEPHONE

MOBILE

E-MAIL


NAME

ADDRESS


TELEPHONE

MOBILE

E-MAIL


NAME

ADDRESS


TELEPHONE

MOBILE

E-MAIL


NAME

ADDRESS


TELEPHONE

MOBILE

E-MAIL


NAME

ADDRESS


TELEPHONE

MOBILE

E-MAIL

NAME

ADDRESS


TELEPHONE

MOBILE

E-MAIL


NAME

ADDRESS


TELEPHONE

MOBILE

E-MAIL


NAME

ADDRESS


TELEPHONE

MOBILE

E-MAIL


NAME

ADDRESS


TELEPHONE

MOBILE

E-MAIL


NAME

ADDRESS


TELEPHONE

MOBILE

E-MAIL


NAME

ADDRESS


TELEPHONE

MOBILE

E-MAIL

NAME

ADDRESS

TELEPHONE

MOBILE

E-MAIL

NAME

ADDRESS

TELEPHONE

MOBILE

E-MAIL

NAME

ADDRESS

TELEPHONE

MOBILE

E-MAIL

NAME

ADDRESS

TELEPHONE

MOBILE

E-MAIL

NAME

ADDRESS

TELEPHONE

MOBILE

E-MAIL

NAME

ADDRESS

TELEPHONE

MOBILE

E-MAIL

NAME

ADDRESS


TELEPHONE

MOBILE

E-MAIL


NAME

ADDRESS


TELEPHONE

MOBILE

E-MAIL


NAME

ADDRESS


TELEPHONE

MOBILE

E-MAIL


NAME

ADDRESS


TELEPHONE

MOBILE

E-MAIL


NAME

ADDRESS


TELEPHONE

MOBILE

E-MAIL


NAME

ADDRESS


TELEPHONE

MOBILE

E-MAIL

NAME

ADDRESS

TELEPHONE

MOBILE

E-MAIL

NAME

ADDRESS

TELEPHONE

MOBILE

E-MAIL

NAME

ADDRESS

TELEPHONE

MOBILE

E-MAIL

NAME

ADDRESS

TELEPHONE

MOBILE

E-MAIL

NAME

ADDRESS

TELEPHONE

MOBILE

E-MAIL

NAME

ADDRESS

TELEPHONE

MOBILE

E-MAIL

| NAME | NAME |
|---|---|
| ADDRESS | ADDRESS |
| | |
| TELEPHONE | TELEPHONE |
| MOBILE | MOBILE |
| E-MAIL | E-MAIL |
| NAME | NAME |
| ADDRESS | ADDRESS |
| | |
| TELEPHONE | TELEPHONE |
| MOBILE | MOBILE |
| E-MAIL | E-MAIL |
| NAME | NAME |
| ADDRESS | ADDRESS |
| | |
| TELEPHONE | TELEPHONE |
| MOBILE | MOBILE |
| E-MAIL | E-MAIL |

NAME

ADDRESS


TELEPHONE

MOBILE

E-MAIL


NAME

ADDRESS


TELEPHONE

MOBILE

E-MAIL


NAME

ADDRESS


TELEPHONE

MOBILE

E-MAIL


NAME

ADDRESS


TELEPHONE

MOBILE

E-MAIL


NAME

ADDRESS


TELEPHONE

MOBILE

E-MAIL


NAME

ADDRESS


TELEPHONE

MOBILE

E-MAIL

NAME

ADDRESS

TELEPHONE

MOBILE

E-MAIL

NAME

ADDRESS

TELEPHONE

MOBILE

E-MAIL

NAME

ADDRESS

TELEPHONE

MOBILE

E-MAIL

NAME

ADDRESS

TELEPHONE

MOBILE

E-MAIL

NAME

ADDRESS

TELEPHONE

MOBILE

E-MAIL

NAME

ADDRESS

TELEPHONE

MOBILE

E-MAIL

| NAME | NAME |
|------|------|
| ADDRESS | ADDRESS |
| | |
| | |
| TELEPHONE | TELEPHONE |
| MOBILE | MOBILE |
| E-MAIL | E-MAIL |
| | |
| NAME | NAME |
| ADDRESS | ADDRESS |
| | |
| | |
| TELEPHONE | TELEPHONE |
| MOBILE | MOBILE |
| E-MAIL | E-MAIL |
| | |
| NAME | NAME |
| ADDRESS | ADDRESS |
| | |
| | |
| TELEPHONE | TELEPHONE |
| MOBILE | MOBILE |
| E-MAIL | E-MAIL |

NAME

ADDRESS

TELEPHONE

MOBILE

E-MAIL

NAME

ADDRESS

TELEPHONE

MOBILE

E-MAIL

NAME

ADDRESS

TELEPHONE

MOBILE

E-MAIL

NAME

ADDRESS

TELEPHONE

MOBILE

E-MAIL

NAME

ADDRESS

TELEPHONE

MOBILE

E-MAIL

NAME

ADDRESS

TELEPHONE

MOBILE

E-MAIL

NAME

ADDRESS

TELEPHONE

MOBILE

E-MAIL

NAME

ADDRESS

TELEPHONE

MOBILE

E-MAIL

NAME

ADDRESS

TELEPHONE

MOBILE

E-MAIL

NAME

ADDRESS

TELEPHONE

MOBILE

E-MAIL

NAME

ADDRESS

TELEPHONE

MOBILE

E-MAIL

NAME

ADDRESS

TELEPHONE

MOBILE

E-MAIL

NAME

ADDRESS


TELEPHONE

MOBILE

E-MAIL


NAME

ADDRESS


TELEPHONE

MOBILE

E-MAIL


NAME

ADDRESS


TELEPHONE

MOBILE

E-MAIL


NAME

ADDRESS


TELEPHONE

MOBILE

E-MAIL


NAME

ADDRESS


TELEPHONE

MOBILE

E-MAIL


NAME

ADDRESS


TELEPHONE

MOBILE

E-MAIL

NAME

ADDRESS


TELEPHONE

MOBILE

E-MAIL


NAME

ADDRESS


TELEPHONE

MOBILE

E-MAIL


NAME

ADDRESS


TELEPHONE

MOBILE

E-MAIL


NAME

ADDRESS


TELEPHONE

MOBILE

E-MAIL


NAME

ADDRESS


TELEPHONE

MOBILE

E-MAIL


NAME

ADDRESS


TELEPHONE

MOBILE

E-MAIL

NAME

ADDRESS


TELEPHONE

MOBILE

E-MAIL


NAME

ADDRESS


TELEPHONE

MOBILE

E-MAIL


NAME

ADDRESS


TELEPHONE

MOBILE

E-MAIL


NAME

ADDRESS


TELEPHONE

MOBILE

E-MAIL


NAME

ADDRESS


TELEPHONE

MOBILE

E-MAIL


NAME

ADDRESS


TELEPHONE

MOBILE

E-MAIL

NAME

ADDRESS


TELEPHONE

MOBILE

E-MAIL


NAME

ADDRESS


TELEPHONE

MOBILE

E-MAIL


NAME

ADDRESS


TELEPHONE

MOBILE

E-MAIL


NAME

ADDRESS


TELEPHONE

MOBILE

E-MAIL


NAME

ADDRESS


TELEPHONE

MOBILE

E-MAIL


NAME

ADDRESS


TELEPHONE

MOBILE

E-MAIL

NAME

ADDRESS


TELEPHONE

MOBILE

E-MAIL


NAME

ADDRESS


TELEPHONE

MOBILE

E-MAIL


NAME

ADDRESS


TELEPHONE

MOBILE

E-MAIL


NAME

ADDRESS


TELEPHONE

MOBILE

E-MAIL


NAME

ADDRESS


TELEPHONE

MOBILE

E-MAIL


NAME

ADDRESS


TELEPHONE

MOBILE

E-MAIL

NAME

ADDRESS


TELEPHONE

MOBILE

E-MAIL


NAME

ADDRESS


TELEPHONE

MOBILE

E-MAIL


NAME

ADDRESS


TELEPHONE

MOBILE

E-MAIL


NAME

ADDRESS


TELEPHONE

MOBILE

E-MAIL


NAME

ADDRESS


TELEPHONE

MOBILE

E-MAIL


NAME

ADDRESS


TELEPHONE

MOBILE

E-MAIL

NAME

ADDRESS


TELEPHONE

MOBILE

E-MAIL


NAME

ADDRESS


TELEPHONE

MOBILE

E-MAIL


NAME

ADDRESS


TELEPHONE

MOBILE

E-MAIL


NAME

ADDRESS


TELEPHONE

MOBILE

E-MAIL


NAME

ADDRESS


TELEPHONE

MOBILE

E-MAIL


NAME

ADDRESS


TELEPHONE

MOBILE

E-MAIL

NAME

ADDRESS


TELEPHONE

MOBILE

E-MAIL


NAME

ADDRESS


TELEPHONE

MOBILE

E-MAIL


NAME

ADDRESS


TELEPHONE

MOBILE

E-MAIL


NAME

ADDRESS


TELEPHONE

MOBILE

E-MAIL


NAME

ADDRESS


TELEPHONE

MOBILE

E-MAIL


NAME

ADDRESS


TELEPHONE

MOBILE

E-MAIL

NAME

ADDRESS



TELEPHONE

MOBILE

E-MAIL


NAME

ADDRESS



TELEPHONE

MOBILE

E-MAIL


NAME

ADDRESS



TELEPHONE

MOBILE

E-MAIL


NAME

ADDRESS



TELEPHONE

MOBILE

E-MAIL


NAME

ADDRESS



TELEPHONE

MOBILE

E-MAIL


NAME

ADDRESS



TELEPHONE

MOBILE

E-MAIL

NAME

ADDRESS


TELEPHONE

MOBILE

E-MAIL


NAME

ADDRESS


TELEPHONE

MOBILE

E-MAIL


NAME

ADDRESS


TELEPHONE

MOBILE

E-MAIL


NAME

ADDRESS


TELEPHONE

MOBILE

E-MAIL


NAME

ADDRESS


TELEPHONE

MOBILE

E-MAIL


NAME

ADDRESS


TELEPHONE

MOBILE

E-MAIL

NAME

ADDRESS


TELEPHONE

MOBILE

E-MAIL


NAME

ADDRESS


TELEPHONE

MOBILE

E-MAIL


NAME

ADDRESS


TELEPHONE

MOBILE

E-MAIL


NAME

ADDRESS


TELEPHONE

MOBILE

E-MAIL


NAME

ADDRESS


TELEPHONE

MOBILE

E-MAIL


NAME

ADDRESS


TELEPHONE

MOBILE

E-MAIL

NAME

ADDRESS


TELEPHONE

MOBILE

E-MAIL


NAME

ADDRESS


TELEPHONE

MOBILE

E-MAIL


NAME

ADDRESS


TELEPHONE

MOBILE

E-MAIL


NAME

ADDRESS


TELEPHONE

MOBILE

E-MAIL


NAME

ADDRESS


TELEPHONE

MOBILE

E-MAIL


NAME

ADDRESS


TELEPHONE

MOBILE

E-MAIL

NAME

ADDRESS


TELEPHONE

MOBILE

E-MAIL


NAME

ADDRESS


TELEPHONE

MOBILE

E-MAIL


NAME

ADDRESS


TELEPHONE

MOBILE

E-MAIL


NAME

ADDRESS


TELEPHONE

MOBILE

E-MAIL


NAME

ADDRESS


TELEPHONE

MOBILE

E-MAIL


NAME

ADDRESS


TELEPHONE

MOBILE

E-MAIL

NAME

ADDRESS


TELEPHONE

MOBILE

E-MAIL


NAME

ADDRESS


TELEPHONE

MOBILE

E-MAIL


NAME

ADDRESS


TELEPHONE

MOBILE

E-MAIL


NAME

ADDRESS


TELEPHONE

MOBILE

E-MAIL


NAME

ADDRESS


TELEPHONE

MOBILE

E-MAIL


NAME

ADDRESS


TELEPHONE

MOBILE

E-MAIL

NAME

ADDRESS


TELEPHONE

MOBILE

E-MAIL


NAME

ADDRESS


TELEPHONE

MOBILE

E-MAIL


NAME

ADDRESS


TELEPHONE

MOBILE

E-MAIL


NAME

ADDRESS


TELEPHONE

MOBILE

E-MAIL


NAME

ADDRESS


TELEPHONE

MOBILE

E-MAIL


NAME

ADDRESS


TELEPHONE

MOBILE

E-MAIL

NAME

ADDRESS

TELEPHONE

MOBILE

E-MAIL

NAME

ADDRESS

TELEPHONE

MOBILE

E-MAIL

NAME

ADDRESS

TELEPHONE

MOBILE

E-MAIL

NAME

ADDRESS

TELEPHONE

MOBILE

E-MAIL

NAME

ADDRESS

TELEPHONE

MOBILE

E-MAIL

NAME

ADDRESS

TELEPHONE

MOBILE

E-MAIL

| NAME | NAME |
| --- | --- |
| ADDRESS | ADDRESS |
| | |
| | |
| TELEPHONE | TELEPHONE |
| MOBILE | MOBILE |
| E-MAIL | E-MAIL |
| | |
| NAME | NAME |
| ADDRESS | ADDRESS |
| | |
| | |
| TELEPHONE | TELEPHONE |
| MOBILE | MOBILE |
| E-MAIL | E-MAIL |
| | |
| NAME | NAME |
| ADDRESS | ADDRESS |
| | |
| | |
| TELEPHONE | TELEPHONE |
| MOBILE | MOBILE |
| E-MAIL | E-MAIL |

| NAME | NAME |
|------|------|
| ADDRESS | ADDRESS |
| | |
| | |
| TELEPHONE | TELEPHONE |
| MOBILE | MOBILE |
| E-MAIL | E-MAIL |
| | |
| NAME | NAME |
| ADDRESS | ADDRESS |
| | |
| | |
| TELEPHONE | TELEPHONE |
| MOBILE | MOBILE |
| E-MAIL | E-MAIL |
| | |
| NAME | NAME |
| ADDRESS | ADDRESS |
| | |
| | |
| TELEPHONE | TELEPHONE |
| MOBILE | MOBILE |
| E-MAIL | E-MAIL |

NAME

ADDRESS


TELEPHONE

MOBILE

E-MAIL


NAME

ADDRESS


TELEPHONE

MOBILE

E-MAIL


NAME

ADDRESS


TELEPHONE

MOBILE

E-MAIL


NAME

ADDRESS


TELEPHONE

MOBILE

E-MAIL


NAME

ADDRESS


TELEPHONE

MOBILE

E-MAIL


NAME

ADDRESS


TELEPHONE

MOBILE

E-MAIL

NAME

ADDRESS


TELEPHONE

MOBILE

E-MAIL


NAME

ADDRESS


TELEPHONE

MOBILE

E-MAIL


NAME

ADDRESS


TELEPHONE

MOBILE

E-MAIL


NAME

ADDRESS


TELEPHONE

MOBILE

E-MAIL


NAME

ADDRESS


TELEPHONE

MOBILE

E-MAIL


NAME

ADDRESS


TELEPHONE

MOBILE

E-MAIL

NAME _____

ADDRESS _____

_____

_____

TELEPHONE _____

MOBILE _____

E-MAIL _____


NAME _____

ADDRESS _____

_____

_____

TELEPHONE _____

MOBILE _____

E-MAIL _____


NAME _____

ADDRESS _____

_____

_____

TELEPHONE _____

MOBILE _____

E-MAIL _____


NAME _____

ADDRESS _____

_____

_____

TELEPHONE _____

MOBILE _____

E-MAIL _____


NAME _____

ADDRESS _____

_____

_____

TELEPHONE _____

MOBILE _____

E-MAIL _____


NAME _____

ADDRESS _____

_____

_____

TELEPHONE _____

MOBILE _____

E-MAIL _____

L

NAME

ADDRESS


TELEPHONE

MOBILE

E-MAIL


NAME

ADDRESS


TELEPHONE

MOBILE

E-MAIL


NAME

ADDRESS


TELEPHONE

MOBILE

E-MAIL


NAME

ADDRESS


TELEPHONE

MOBILE

E-MAIL


NAME

ADDRESS


TELEPHONE

MOBILE

E-MAIL


NAME

ADDRESS


TELEPHONE

MOBILE

E-MAIL

M

| NAME | NAME |
|------|------|
| ADDRESS | ADDRESS |
| | |
| TELEPHONE | TELEPHONE |
| MOBILE | MOBILE |
| E-MAIL | E-MAIL |
| | |
| NAME | NAME |
| ADDRESS | ADDRESS |
| | |
| TELEPHONE | TELEPHONE |
| MOBILE | MOBILE |
| E-MAIL | E-MAIL |
| | |
| NAME | NAME |
| ADDRESS | ADDRESS |
| | |
| TELEPHONE | TELEPHONE |
| MOBILE | MOBILE |
| E-MAIL | E-MAIL |

NAME

ADDRESS

TELEPHONE

MOBILE

E-MAIL


NAME

ADDRESS

TELEPHONE

MOBILE

E-MAIL


NAME

ADDRESS

TELEPHONE

MOBILE

E-MAIL


NAME

ADDRESS

TELEPHONE

MOBILE

E-MAIL


NAME

ADDRESS

TELEPHONE

MOBILE

E-MAIL


NAME

ADDRESS

TELEPHONE

MOBILE

E-MAIL

NAME _____

ADDRESS _____

_____

_____

TELEPHONE _____

MOBILE _____

E-MAIL _____

NAME _____

ADDRESS _____

_____

_____

TELEPHONE _____

MOBILE _____

E-MAIL _____

NAME _____

ADDRESS _____

_____

_____

TELEPHONE _____

MOBILE _____

E-MAIL _____

NAME _____

ADDRESS _____

_____

_____

TELEPHONE _____

MOBILE _____

E-MAIL _____

NAME _____

ADDRESS _____

_____

_____

TELEPHONE _____

MOBILE _____

E-MAIL _____

NAME _____

ADDRESS _____

_____

_____

TELEPHONE _____

MOBILE _____

E-MAIL _____

NAME

ADDRESS


TELEPHONE

MOBILE

E-MAIL


NAME

ADDRESS


TELEPHONE

MOBILE

E-MAIL


NAME

ADDRESS


TELEPHONE

MOBILE

E-MAIL


NAME

ADDRESS


TELEPHONE

MOBILE

E-MAIL


NAME

ADDRESS


TELEPHONE

MOBILE

E-MAIL


NAME

ADDRESS


TELEPHONE

MOBILE

E-MAIL

NAME

ADDRESS


TELEPHONE

MOBILE

E-MAIL


NAME

ADDRESS


TELEPHONE

MOBILE

E-MAIL


NAME

ADDRESS


TELEPHONE

MOBILE

E-MAIL

NAME

ADDRESS


TELEPHONE

MOBILE

E-MAIL


NAME

ADDRESS


TELEPHONE

MOBILE

E-MAIL


NAME

ADDRESS


TELEPHONE

MOBILE

E-MAIL

NAME

ADDRESS


TELEPHONE

MOBILE

E-MAIL


NAME

ADDRESS


TELEPHONE

MOBILE

E-MAIL


NAME

ADDRESS


TELEPHONE

MOBILE

E-MAIL


NAME

ADDRESS


TELEPHONE

MOBILE

E-MAIL


NAME

ADDRESS


TELEPHONE

MOBILE

E-MAIL


NAME

ADDRESS


TELEPHONE

MOBILE

E-MAIL

| NAME | NAME |
|---|---|
| ADDRESS | ADDRESS |
| | |
| | |
| TELEPHONE | TELEPHONE |
| MOBILE | MOBILE |
| E-MAIL | E-MAIL |
| | |
| NAME | NAME |
| ADDRESS | ADDRESS |
| | |
| | |
| TELEPHONE | TELEPHONE |
| MOBILE | MOBILE |
| E-MAIL | E-MAIL |
| | |
| NAME | NAME |
| ADDRESS | ADDRESS |
| | |
| | |
| TELEPHONE | TELEPHONE |
| MOBILE | MOBILE |
| E-MAIL | E-MAIL |

NAME

ADDRESS


TELEPHONE

MOBILE

E-MAIL


NAME

ADDRESS


TELEPHONE

MOBILE

E-MAIL


NAME

ADDRESS


TELEPHONE

MOBILE

E-MAIL


NAME

ADDRESS


TELEPHONE

MOBILE

E-MAIL


NAME

ADDRESS


TELEPHONE

MOBILE

E-MAIL


NAME

ADDRESS


TELEPHONE

MOBILE

E-MAIL

NAME

ADDRESS


TELEPHONE

MOBILE

E-MAIL


NAME

ADDRESS


TELEPHONE

MOBILE

E-MAIL


NAME

ADDRESS


TELEPHONE

MOBILE

E-MAIL


NAME

ADDRESS


TELEPHONE

MOBILE

E-MAIL


NAME

ADDRESS


TELEPHONE

MOBILE

E-MAIL


NAME

ADDRESS


TELEPHONE

MOBILE

E-MAIL

P

NAME

ADDRESS


TELEPHONE

MOBILE

E-MAIL


NAME

ADDRESS


TELEPHONE

MOBILE

E-MAIL


NAME

ADDRESS


TELEPHONE

MOBILE

E-MAIL


NAME

ADDRESS


TELEPHONE

MOBILE

E-MAIL


NAME

ADDRESS


TELEPHONE

MOBILE

E-MAIL


NAME

ADDRESS


TELEPHONE

MOBILE

E-MAIL

P

NAME

ADDRESS


TELEPHONE

MOBILE

E-MAIL


NAME

ADDRESS


TELEPHONE

MOBILE

E-MAIL


NAME

ADDRESS


TELEPHONE

MOBILE

E-MAIL


NAME

ADDRESS


TELEPHONE

MOBILE

E-MAIL


NAME

ADDRESS


TELEPHONE

MOBILE

E-MAIL


NAME

ADDRESS


TELEPHONE

MOBILE

E-MAIL

P

NAME

ADDRESS


TELEPHONE

MOBILE

E-MAIL


NAME

ADDRESS


TELEPHONE

MOBILE

E-MAIL


NAME

ADDRESS


TELEPHONE

MOBILE

E-MAIL


NAME

ADDRESS


TELEPHONE

MOBILE

E-MAIL


NAME

ADDRESS


TELEPHONE

MOBILE

E-MAIL


NAME

ADDRESS


TELEPHONE

MOBILE

E-MAIL

Q

NAME

ADDRESS

TELEPHONE

MOBILE

E-MAIL


NAME

ADDRESS

TELEPHONE

MOBILE

E-MAIL


NAME

ADDRESS

TELEPHONE

MOBILE

E-MAIL


NAME

ADDRESS

TELEPHONE

MOBILE

E-MAIL


NAME

ADDRESS

TELEPHONE

MOBILE

E-MAIL


NAME

ADDRESS

TELEPHONE

MOBILE

E-MAIL

Q

NAME

ADDRESS


TELEPHONE

MOBILE

E-MAIL


NAME

ADDRESS


TELEPHONE

MOBILE

E-MAIL


NAME

ADDRESS


TELEPHONE

MOBILE

E-MAIL


NAME

ADDRESS


TELEPHONE

MOBILE

E-MAIL


NAME

ADDRESS


TELEPHONE

MOBILE

E-MAIL


NAME

ADDRESS


TELEPHONE

MOBILE

E-MAIL

Q

| NAME | NAME |
|------|------|
| ADDRESS | ADDRESS |
| | |
| | |
| TELEPHONE | TELEPHONE |
| MOBILE | MOBILE |
| E-MAIL | E-MAIL |
| | |
| NAME | NAME |
| ADDRESS | ADDRESS |
| | |
| | |
| TELEPHONE | TELEPHONE |
| MOBILE | MOBILE |
| E-MAIL | E-MAIL |
| | |
| NAME | NAME |
| ADDRESS | ADDRESS |
| | |
| | |
| TELEPHONE | TELEPHONE |
| MOBILE | MOBILE |
| E-MAIL | E-MAIL |

NAME

ADDRESS

TELEPHONE

MOBILE

E-MAIL

NAME

ADDRESS

TELEPHONE

MOBILE

E-MAIL

NAME

ADDRESS

TELEPHONE

MOBILE

E-MAIL

NAME

ADDRESS

TELEPHONE

MOBILE

E-MAIL

NAME

ADDRESS

TELEPHONE

MOBILE

E-MAIL

NAME

ADDRESS

TELEPHONE

MOBILE

E-MAIL

NAME

ADDRESS


TELEPHONE

MOBILE

E-MAIL


NAME

ADDRESS


TELEPHONE

MOBILE

E-MAIL


NAME

ADDRESS


TELEPHONE

MOBILE

E-MAIL

NAME

ADDRESS


TELEPHONE

MOBILE

E-MAIL


NAME

ADDRESS


TELEPHONE

MOBILE

E-MAIL


NAME

ADDRESS


TELEPHONE

MOBILE

E-MAIL

R

NAME

ADDRESS


TELEPHONE

MOBILE

E-MAIL


NAME

ADDRESS


TELEPHONE

MOBILE

E-MAIL


NAME

ADDRESS


TELEPHONE

MOBILE

E-MAIL

NAME

ADDRESS


TELEPHONE

MOBILE

E-MAIL


NAME

ADDRESS


TELEPHONE

MOBILE

E-MAIL


NAME

ADDRESS


TELEPHONE

MOBILE

E-MAIL

NAME

ADDRESS


TELEPHONE

MOBILE

E-MAIL


NAME

ADDRESS


TELEPHONE

MOBILE

E-MAIL


NAME

ADDRESS


TELEPHONE

MOBILE

E-MAIL


NAME

ADDRESS


TELEPHONE

MOBILE

E-MAIL


NAME

ADDRESS


TELEPHONE

MOBILE

E-MAIL


NAME

ADDRESS


TELEPHONE

MOBILE

E-MAIL

NAME

ADDRESS

TELEPHONE

MOBILE

E-MAIL

NAME

ADDRESS

TELEPHONE

MOBILE

E-MAIL

NAME

ADDRESS

TELEPHONE

MOBILE

E-MAIL

NAME

ADDRESS

TELEPHONE

MOBILE

E-MAIL

NAME

ADDRESS

TELEPHONE

MOBILE

E-MAIL

NAME

ADDRESS

TELEPHONE

MOBILE

E-MAIL

NAME

ADDRESS

TELEPHONE

MOBILE

E-MAIL

NAME

ADDRESS

TELEPHONE

MOBILE

E-MAIL

NAME

ADDRESS

TELEPHONE

MOBILE

E-MAIL

NAME

ADDRESS

TELEPHONE

MOBILE

E-MAIL

NAME

ADDRESS

TELEPHONE

MOBILE

E-MAIL

NAME

ADDRESS

TELEPHONE

MOBILE

E-MAIL

T

NAME

ADDRESS


TELEPHONE

MOBILE

E-MAIL


NAME

ADDRESS


TELEPHONE

MOBILE

E-MAIL


NAME

ADDRESS


TELEPHONE

MOBILE

E-MAIL


NAME

ADDRESS


TELEPHONE

MOBILE

E-MAIL


NAME

ADDRESS


TELEPHONE

MOBILE

E-MAIL


NAME

ADDRESS


TELEPHONE

MOBILE

E-MAIL

| NAME | NAME |
|------|------|
| ADDRESS | ADDRESS |
| | |
| TELEPHONE | TELEPHONE |
| MOBILE | MOBILE |
| E-MAIL | E-MAIL |

| NAME | NAME |
|------|------|
| ADDRESS | ADDRESS |
| | |
| TELEPHONE | TELEPHONE |
| MOBILE | MOBILE |
| E-MAIL | E-MAIL |

| NAME | NAME |
|------|------|
| ADDRESS | ADDRESS |
| | |
| TELEPHONE | TELEPHONE |
| MOBILE | MOBILE |
| E-MAIL | E-MAIL |

T

NAME

ADDRESS


TELEPHONE

MOBILE

E-MAIL


NAME

ADDRESS


TELEPHONE

MOBILE

E-MAIL


NAME

ADDRESS


TELEPHONE

MOBILE

E-MAIL


NAME

ADDRESS


TELEPHONE

MOBILE

E-MAIL


NAME

ADDRESS


TELEPHONE

MOBILE

E-MAIL


NAME

ADDRESS


TELEPHONE

MOBILE

E-MAIL

NAME

ADDRESS

TELEPHONE

MOBILE

E-MAIL

NAME

ADDRESS

TELEPHONE

MOBILE

E-MAIL

NAME

ADDRESS

TELEPHONE

MOBILE

E-MAIL

NAME

ADDRESS

TELEPHONE

MOBILE

E-MAIL

NAME

ADDRESS

TELEPHONE

MOBILE

E-MAIL

NAME

ADDRESS

TELEPHONE

MOBILE

E-MAIL

NAME

ADDRESS


TELEPHONE

MOBILE

E-MAIL


NAME

ADDRESS


TELEPHONE

MOBILE

E-MAIL


NAME

ADDRESS


TELEPHONE

MOBILE

E-MAIL


NAME

ADDRESS


TELEPHONE

MOBILE

E-MAIL


NAME

ADDRESS


TELEPHONE

MOBILE

E-MAIL


NAME

ADDRESS


TELEPHONE

MOBILE

E-MAIL

NAME

ADDRESS


TELEPHONE

MOBILE

E-MAIL


NAME

ADDRESS


TELEPHONE

MOBILE

E-MAIL


NAME

ADDRESS


TELEPHONE

MOBILE

E-MAIL


NAME

ADDRESS


TELEPHONE

MOBILE

E-MAIL


NAME

ADDRESS


TELEPHONE

MOBILE

E-MAIL


NAME

ADDRESS


TELEPHONE

MOBILE

E-MAIL

NAME

ADDRESS


TELEPHONE

MOBILE

E-MAIL


NAME

ADDRESS


TELEPHONE

MOBILE

E-MAIL


NAME

ADDRESS


TELEPHONE

MOBILE

E-MAIL


NAME

ADDRESS


TELEPHONE

MOBILE

E-MAIL


NAME

ADDRESS


TELEPHONE

MOBILE

E-MAIL


NAME

ADDRESS


TELEPHONE

MOBILE

E-MAIL

NAME

ADDRESS


TELEPHONE

MOBILE

E-MAIL


NAME

ADDRESS


TELEPHONE

MOBILE

E-MAIL


NAME

ADDRESS


TELEPHONE

MOBILE

E-MAIL


NAME

ADDRESS


TELEPHONE

MOBILE

E-MAIL


NAME

ADDRESS


TELEPHONE

MOBILE

E-MAIL


NAME

ADDRESS


TELEPHONE

MOBILE

E-MAIL

NAME

ADDRESS


TELEPHONE

MOBILE

E-MAIL


NAME

ADDRESS


TELEPHONE

MOBILE

E-MAIL


NAME

ADDRESS


TELEPHONE

MOBILE

E-MAIL


NAME

ADDRESS


TELEPHONE

MOBILE

E-MAIL


NAME

ADDRESS


TELEPHONE

MOBILE

E-MAIL


NAME

ADDRESS


TELEPHONE

MOBILE

E-MAIL

| NAME | NAME |
|------|------|
| ADDRESS | ADDRESS |
| | |
| | |
| TELEPHONE | TELEPHONE |
| MOBILE | MOBILE |
| E-MAIL | E-MAIL |
| | |
| NAME | NAME |
| ADDRESS | ADDRESS |
| | |
| | |
| TELEPHONE | TELEPHONE |
| MOBILE | MOBILE |
| E-MAIL | E-MAIL |
| | |
| NAME | NAME |
| ADDRESS | ADDRESS |
| | |
| | |
| TELEPHONE | TELEPHONE |
| MOBILE | MOBILE |
| E-MAIL | E-MAIL |

NAME

ADDRESS

TELEPHONE

MOBILE

E-MAIL

NAME

ADDRESS

TELEPHONE

MOBILE

E-MAIL

NAME

ADDRESS

TELEPHONE

MOBILE

E-MAIL

NAME

ADDRESS

TELEPHONE

MOBILE

E-MAIL

NAME

ADDRESS

TELEPHONE

MOBILE

E-MAIL

NAME

ADDRESS

TELEPHONE

MOBILE

E-MAIL

X

NAME

ADDRESS


TELEPHONE

MOBILE

E-MAIL


NAME

ADDRESS


TELEPHONE

MOBILE

E-MAIL


NAME

ADDRESS


TELEPHONE

MOBILE

E-MAIL


NAME

ADDRESS


TELEPHONE

MOBILE

E-MAIL


NAME

ADDRESS


TELEPHONE

MOBILE

E-MAIL


NAME

ADDRESS


TELEPHONE

MOBILE

E-MAIL

*Birthdays, Events & Anniversaries*

# January

| | | | |
|---|---|---|---|
| 1 | 2 | 3 | 4 |
| 5 | 6 | 7 | 8 |
| 9 | 10 | 11 | 12 |
| 13 | 14 | 15 | 16 |

# January

| 17 | 18 | 19 | 20 |
|----|----|----|----|
| 21 | 22 | 23 | 24 |
| 25 | 26 | 27 | 28 |
| 29 | 30 | 31 | |

# February

| | | | |
|---|---|---|---|
| 1 | 2 | 3 | 4 |
| 5 | 6 | 7 | 8 |
| 9 | 10 | 11 | 12 |
| 13 | 14 | 15 | 16 |

## FEBRUARY

| 17 | 18 | 19 | 20 |
|----|----|----|----|
| 21 | 22 | 23 | 24 |
| 25 | 26 | 27 | 28 |
| 29 |  |  |  |

# MARCH

| 1 | 2 | 3 | 4 |
|---|---|---|---|
| 5 | 6 | 7 | 8 |
| 9 | 10 | 11 | 12 |
| 13 | 14 | 15 | 16 |

## MARCH

| 17 | 18 | 19 | 20 |
|----|----|----|----|
| 21 | 22 | 23 | 24 |
| 25 | 26 | 27 | 28 |
| 29 | 30 | 31 | |

# APRIL

| 1 | 2 | 3 | 4 |
|---|---|---|---|
| 5 | 6 | 7 | 8 |
| 9 | 10 | 11 | 12 |
| 13 | 14 | 15 | 16 |

## APRIL

| 17 | 18 | 19 | 20 |
|----|----|----|----|
| 21 | 22 | 23 | 24 |
| 25 | 26 | 27 | 28 |
| 29 | 30 | | |

# MAY

| 1 | 2 | 3 | 4 |
| 5 | 6 | 7 | 8 |
| 9 | 10 | 11 | 12 |
| 13 | 14 | 15 | 16 |

# MAY

| 17 | 18 | 19 | 20 |
|----|----|----|----|
| 21 | 22 | 23 | 24 |
| 25 | 26 | 27 | 28 |
| 29 | 30 | 31 | |

# JUNE

| | | | |
|---|---|---|---|
| 1 | 2 | 3 | 4 |
| 5 | 6 | 7 | 8 |
| 9 | 10 | 11 | 12 |
| 13 | 14 | 15 | 16 |

# JUNE

| 17 | 18 | 19 | 20 |
|----|----|----|----|
| 21 | 22 | 23 | 24 |
| 25 | 26 | 27 | 28 |
| 29 | 30 | | |

# JULY

| 1 | 2 | 3 | 4 |
|---|---|---|---|
| 5 | 6 | 7 | 8 |
| 9 | 10 | 11 | 12 |
| 13 | 14 | 15 | 16 |

## JULY

| 17 | 18 | 19 | 20 |
|----|----|----|----|
| 21 | 22 | 23 | 24 |
| 25 | 26 | 27 | 28 |
| 29 | 30 | 31 | |

# AUGUST

| | | | |
|---|---|---|---|
| 1 | 2 | 3 | 4 |
| 5 | 6 | 7 | 8 |
| 9 | 10 | 11 | 12 |
| 13 | 14 | 15 | 16 |

## AUGUST

| | | | |
|---|---|---|---|
| 17 | 18 | 19 | 20 |
| 21 | 22 | 23 | 24 |
| 25 | 26 | 27 | 28 |
| 29 | 30 | 31 | |

# September

| | | | |
|---|---|---|---|
| 1 | 2 | 3 | 4 |
| 5 | 6 | 7 | 8 |
| 9 | 10 | 11 | 12 |
| 13 | 14 | 15 | 16 |

## SEPTEMBER

| 17 | 18 | 19 | 20 |
|---|---|---|---|
| 21 | 22 | 23 | 24 |
| 25 | 26 | 27 | 28 |
| 29 | 30 | | |

# OCTOBER

| | | | |
|---|---|---|---|
| 1 | 2 | 3 | 4 |
| 5 | 6 | 7 | 8 |
| 9 | 10 | 11 | 12 |
| 13 | 14 | 15 | 16 |

# OCTOBER

| | | | |
|---|---|---|---|
| 17 | 18 | 19 | 20 |
| 21 | 22 | 23 | 24 |
| 25 | 26 | 27 | 28 |
| 29 | 30 | 31 | |

# November

| | | | |
|---|---|---|---|
| 1 | 2 | 3 | 4 |
| 5 | 6 | 7 | 8 |
| 9 | 10 | 11 | 12 |
| 13 | 14 | 15 | 16 |

## NOVEMBER

| 17 | 18 | 19 | 20 |
|----|----|----|----|
| 21 | 22 | 23 | 24 |
| 25 | 26 | 27 | 28 |
| 29 | 30 | | |

# DECEMBER

| 1 | 2 | 3 | 4 |
|---|---|---|---|
| 5 | 6 | 7 | 8 |
| 9 | 10 | 11 | 12 |
| 13 | 14 | 15 | 16 |

# December

| 17 | 18 | 19 | 20 |
|----|----|----|----|
| 21 | 22 | 23 | 24 |
| 25 | 26 | 27 | 28 |
| 29 | 30 | 31 | |

*Christmas Card List*

| Name | Year | Sent | Received |
|------|------|------|----------|
|      |      |      |          |
|      |      |      |          |
|      |      |      |          |
|      |      |      |          |
|      |      |      |          |
|      |      |      |          |
|      |      |      |          |
|      |      |      |          |
|      |      |      |          |
|      |      |      |          |
|      |      |      |          |
|      |      |      |          |
|      |      |      |          |
|      |      |      |          |
|      |      |      |          |
|      |      |      |          |
|      |      |      |          |
|      |      |      |          |
|      |      |      |          |
|      |      |      |          |
|      |      |      |          |
|      |      |      |          |
|      |      |      |          |

| NAME | YEAR | SENT | RECEIVED |
|------|------|------|----------|
|      |      |      |          |
|      |      |      |          |
|      |      |      |          |
|      |      |      |          |
|      |      |      |          |
|      |      |      |          |
|      |      |      |          |
|      |      |      |          |
|      |      |      |          |
|      |      |      |          |
|      |      |      |          |
|      |      |      |          |
|      |      |      |          |
|      |      |      |          |
|      |      |      |          |
|      |      |      |          |
|      |      |      |          |
|      |      |      |          |
|      |      |      |          |
|      |      |      |          |
|      |      |      |          |
|      |      |      |          |
|      |      |      |          |
|      |      |      |          |

| Name | Year | Sent | Received |
|------|------|------|----------|
|      |      |      |          |
|      |      |      |          |
|      |      |      |          |
|      |      |      |          |
|      |      |      |          |
|      |      |      |          |
|      |      |      |          |
|      |      |      |          |
|      |      |      |          |
|      |      |      |          |
|      |      |      |          |
|      |      |      |          |
|      |      |      |          |
|      |      |      |          |
|      |      |      |          |
|      |      |      |          |
|      |      |      |          |
|      |      |      |          |
|      |      |      |          |
|      |      |      |          |
|      |      |      |          |
|      |      |      |          |
|      |      |      |          |
|      |      |      |          |
|      |      |      |          |

| NAME | YEAR | SENT | RECEIVED |
|------|------|------|----------|
|      |      |      |          |
|      |      |      |          |
|      |      |      |          |
|      |      |      |          |
|      |      |      |          |
|      |      |      |          |
|      |      |      |          |
|      |      |      |          |
|      |      |      |          |
|      |      |      |          |
|      |      |      |          |
|      |      |      |          |
|      |      |      |          |
|      |      |      |          |
|      |      |      |          |
|      |      |      |          |
|      |      |      |          |
|      |      |      |          |
|      |      |      |          |
|      |      |      |          |
|      |      |      |          |
|      |      |      |          |
|      |      |      |          |
|      |      |      |          |
|      |      |      |          |
|      |      |      |          |
|      |      |      |          |
|      |      |      |          |

| Name | Year | Sent | Received |
|------|------|------|----------|
|  |  |  |  |
|  |  |  |  |
|  |  |  |  |
|  |  |  |  |
|  |  |  |  |
|  |  |  |  |
|  |  |  |  |
|  |  |  |  |
|  |  |  |  |
|  |  |  |  |
|  |  |  |  |
|  |  |  |  |
|  |  |  |  |
|  |  |  |  |
|  |  |  |  |
|  |  |  |  |
|  |  |  |  |
|  |  |  |  |
|  |  |  |  |
|  |  |  |  |
|  |  |  |  |
|  |  |  |  |
|  |  |  |  |
|  |  |  |  |

# CHRISTMAS CARD LIST

| Name | Year | Sent | Received |
|------|------|------|----------|
|  |  |  |  |
|  |  |  |  |
|  |  |  |  |
|  |  |  |  |
|  |  |  |  |
|  |  |  |  |
|  |  |  |  |
|  |  |  |  |
|  |  |  |  |
|  |  |  |  |
|  |  |  |  |
|  |  |  |  |
|  |  |  |  |
|  |  |  |  |
|  |  |  |  |
|  |  |  |  |
|  |  |  |  |
|  |  |  |  |
|  |  |  |  |
|  |  |  |  |
|  |  |  |  |
|  |  |  |  |
|  |  |  |  |
|  |  |  |  |
|  |  |  |  |
|  |  |  |  |

| Name | Year | Sent | Received |
|------|------|------|----------|
|      |      |      |          |
|      |      |      |          |
|      |      |      |          |
|      |      |      |          |
|      |      |      |          |
|      |      |      |          |
|      |      |      |          |
|      |      |      |          |
|      |      |      |          |
|      |      |      |          |
|      |      |      |          |
|      |      |      |          |
|      |      |      |          |
|      |      |      |          |
|      |      |      |          |
|      |      |      |          |
|      |      |      |          |
|      |      |      |          |
|      |      |      |          |
|      |      |      |          |
|      |      |      |          |
|      |      |      |          |
|      |      |      |          |
|      |      |      |          |

# CHRISTMAS CARD LIST

| NAME | YEAR | SENT | RECEIVED |
|------|------|------|----------|
|      |      |      |          |
|      |      |      |          |
|      |      |      |          |
|      |      |      |          |
|      |      |      |          |
|      |      |      |          |
|      |      |      |          |
|      |      |      |          |
|      |      |      |          |
|      |      |      |          |
|      |      |      |          |
|      |      |      |          |
|      |      |      |          |
|      |      |      |          |
|      |      |      |          |
|      |      |      |          |
|      |      |      |          |
|      |      |      |          |
|      |      |      |          |
|      |      |      |          |
|      |      |      |          |
|      |      |      |          |
|      |      |      |          |
|      |      |      |          |

| Name | Year | Sent | Received |
|------|------|------|----------|
|      |      |      |          |
|      |      |      |          |
|      |      |      |          |
|      |      |      |          |
|      |      |      |          |
|      |      |      |          |
|      |      |      |          |
|      |      |      |          |
|      |      |      |          |
|      |      |      |          |
|      |      |      |          |
|      |      |      |          |
|      |      |      |          |
|      |      |      |          |
|      |      |      |          |
|      |      |      |          |
|      |      |      |          |
|      |      |      |          |
|      |      |      |          |
|      |      |      |          |
|      |      |      |          |
|      |      |      |          |
|      |      |      |          |
|      |      |      |          |
|      |      |      |          |
|      |      |      |          |
|      |      |      |          |
|      |      |      |          |
|      |      |      |          |
|      |      |      |          |

# CHRISTMAS CARD LIST

| Name | Year | Sent | Received |
|------|------|------|----------|
|      |      |      |          |
|      |      |      |          |
|      |      |      |          |
|      |      |      |          |
|      |      |      |          |
|      |      |      |          |
|      |      |      |          |
|      |      |      |          |
|      |      |      |          |
|      |      |      |          |
|      |      |      |          |
|      |      |      |          |
|      |      |      |          |
|      |      |      |          |
|      |      |      |          |
|      |      |      |          |
|      |      |      |          |
|      |      |      |          |
|      |      |      |          |
|      |      |      |          |
|      |      |      |          |
|      |      |      |          |
|      |      |      |          |
|      |      |      |          |
|      |      |      |          |
|      |      |      |          |

| NAME | YEAR | SENT | RECEIVED |
|------|------|------|----------|
|      |      |      |          |
|      |      |      |          |
|      |      |      |          |
|      |      |      |          |
|      |      |      |          |
|      |      |      |          |
|      |      |      |          |
|      |      |      |          |
|      |      |      |          |
|      |      |      |          |
|      |      |      |          |
|      |      |      |          |
|      |      |      |          |
|      |      |      |          |
|      |      |      |          |
|      |      |      |          |
|      |      |      |          |
|      |      |      |          |
|      |      |      |          |
|      |      |      |          |
|      |      |      |          |
|      |      |      |          |
|      |      |      |          |
|      |      |      |          |
|      |      |      |          |
|      |      |      |          |

# CHRISTMAS CARD LIST

| NAME | YEAR | SENT | RECEIVED |
|------|------|------|----------|
|      |      |      |          |
|      |      |      |          |
|      |      |      |          |
|      |      |      |          |
|      |      |      |          |
|      |      |      |          |
|      |      |      |          |
|      |      |      |          |
|      |      |      |          |
|      |      |      |          |
|      |      |      |          |
|      |      |      |          |
|      |      |      |          |
|      |      |      |          |
|      |      |      |          |
|      |      |      |          |
|      |      |      |          |
|      |      |      |          |
|      |      |      |          |
|      |      |      |          |
|      |      |      |          |
|      |      |      |          |
|      |      |      |          |
|      |      |      |          |
|      |      |      |          |
|      |      |      |          |
|      |      |      |          |

| Name | Year | Sent | Received |
|------|------|------|----------|
|      |      |      |          |
|      |      |      |          |
|      |      |      |          |
|      |      |      |          |
|      |      |      |          |
|      |      |      |          |
|      |      |      |          |
|      |      |      |          |
|      |      |      |          |
|      |      |      |          |
|      |      |      |          |
|      |      |      |          |
|      |      |      |          |
|      |      |      |          |
|      |      |      |          |
|      |      |      |          |
|      |      |      |          |
|      |      |      |          |
|      |      |      |          |
|      |      |      |          |
|      |      |      |          |
|      |      |      |          |
|      |      |      |          |

| NAME | YEAR | SENT | RECEIVED |
|------|------|------|----------|
|      |      |      |          |
|      |      |      |          |
|      |      |      |          |
|      |      |      |          |
|      |      |      |          |
|      |      |      |          |
|      |      |      |          |
|      |      |      |          |
|      |      |      |          |
|      |      |      |          |
|      |      |      |          |
|      |      |      |          |
|      |      |      |          |
|      |      |      |          |
|      |      |      |          |
|      |      |      |          |
|      |      |      |          |
|      |      |      |          |
|      |      |      |          |
|      |      |      |          |
|      |      |      |          |
|      |      |      |          |
|      |      |      |          |
|      |      |      |          |
|      |      |      |          |
|      |      |      |          |
|      |      |      |          |
|      |      |      |          |
|      |      |      |          |
|      |      |      |          |
|      |      |      |          |

| Name | Year | Sent | Received |
|------|------|------|----------|
|      |      |      |          |
|      |      |      |          |
|      |      |      |          |
|      |      |      |          |
|      |      |      |          |
|      |      |      |          |
|      |      |      |          |
|      |      |      |          |
|      |      |      |          |
|      |      |      |          |
|      |      |      |          |
|      |      |      |          |
|      |      |      |          |
|      |      |      |          |
|      |      |      |          |
|      |      |      |          |
|      |      |      |          |
|      |      |      |          |
|      |      |      |          |
|      |      |      |          |
|      |      |      |          |
|      |      |      |          |
|      |      |      |          |
|      |      |      |          |
|      |      |      |          |
|      |      |      |          |

# CHRISTMAS CARD LIST

| Name | Year | Sent | Received |
|------|------|------|----------|
|      |      |      |          |
|      |      |      |          |
|      |      |      |          |
|      |      |      |          |
|      |      |      |          |
|      |      |      |          |
|      |      |      |          |
|      |      |      |          |
|      |      |      |          |
|      |      |      |          |
|      |      |      |          |
|      |      |      |          |
|      |      |      |          |
|      |      |      |          |
|      |      |      |          |
|      |      |      |          |
|      |      |      |          |
|      |      |      |          |
|      |      |      |          |
|      |      |      |          |
|      |      |      |          |

## Gifts & Ideas List

| Name | Occasion | Date |
| --- | --- | --- |
| | | |
| | | |
| | | |
| | | |
| | | |
| | | |
| | | |
| | | |
| | | |
| | | |
| | | |
| | | |
| | | |
| | | |
| | | |
| | | |
| | | |
| | | |
| | | |

| NAME | OCCASION | DATE |
|------|----------|------|
| | | |
| | | |
| | | |
| | | |
| | | |
| | | |
| | | |
| | | |
| | | |
| | | |
| | | |
| | | |
| | | |
| | | |
| | | |
| | | |
| | | |
| | | |
| | | |
| | | |
| | | |
| | | |
| | | |
| | | |
| | | |
| | | |

| Name | Occasion | Date |
| --- | --- | --- |
| | | |
| | | |
| | | |
| | | |
| | | |
| | | |
| | | |
| | | |
| | | |
| | | |
| | | |
| | | |
| | | |
| | | |
| | | |
| | | |
| | | |
| | | |
| | | |

| Name | Occasion | Date |
| --- | --- | --- |
| | | |
| | | |
| | | |
| | | |
| | | |
| | | |
| | | |
| | | |
| | | |
| | | |
| | | |
| | | |
| | | |
| | | |
| | | |
| | | |
| | | |
| | | |
| | | |
| | | |
| | | |
| | | |
| | | |

| Name | Occasion | Date |
|------|----------|------|
|      |          |      |
|      |          |      |
|      |          |      |
|      |          |      |
|      |          |      |
|      |          |      |
|      |          |      |
|      |          |      |
|      |          |      |
|      |          |      |
|      |          |      |
|      |          |      |
|      |          |      |
|      |          |      |
|      |          |      |
|      |          |      |
|      |          |      |
|      |          |      |
|      |          |      |
|      |          |      |

GIFTS & IDEAS LIST

| NAME | OCCASION | DATE |
|------|----------|------|
|      |          |      |

| Name | Occasion | Date |
|------|----------|------|
|  |  |  |
|  |  |  |
|  |  |  |
|  |  |  |
|  |  |  |
|  |  |  |
|  |  |  |
|  |  |  |
|  |  |  |
|  |  |  |
|  |  |  |
|  |  |  |
|  |  |  |
|  |  |  |
|  |  |  |
|  |  |  |
|  |  |  |
|  |  |  |
|  |  |  |
|  |  |  |

| Name | Occasion | Date |
|------|----------|------|
| | | |
| | | |
| | | |
| | | |
| | | |
| | | |
| | | |
| | | |
| | | |
| | | |
| | | |
| | | |
| | | |
| | | |
| | | |
| | | |
| | | |
| | | |
| | | |
| | | |
| | | |

| NAME | OCCASION | DATE |
|------|----------|------|
| | | |
| | | |
| | | |
| | | |
| | | |
| | | |
| | | |
| | | |
| | | |
| | | |
| | | |
| | | |
| | | |
| | | |
| | | |
| | | |
| | | |
| | | |
| | | |
| | | |
| | | |

| Name | Occasion | Date |
|------|----------|------|
| | | |
| | | |
| | | |
| | | |
| | | |
| | | |
| | | |
| | | |
| | | |
| | | |
| | | |
| | | |
| | | |
| | | |
| | | |
| | | |
| | | |
| | | |
| | | |
| | | |
| | | |
| | | |

| Name | Occasion | Date |
| --- | --- | --- |
| | | |
| | | |
| | | |
| | | |
| | | |
| | | |
| | | |
| | | |
| | | |
| | | |
| | | |
| | | |
| | | |
| | | |
| | | |
| | | |
| | | |
| | | |
| | | |
| | | |

| NAME | OCCASION | DATE |
|------|----------|------|
| | | |
| | | |
| | | |
| | | |
| | | |
| | | |
| | | |
| | | |
| | | |
| | | |
| | | |
| | | |
| | | |
| | | |
| | | |
| | | |
| | | |
| | | |
| | | |
| | | |

| NAME | OCCASION | DATE |
|------|----------|------|
|  |  |  |
|  |  |  |
|  |  |  |
|  |  |  |
|  |  |  |
|  |  |  |
|  |  |  |
|  |  |  |
|  |  |  |
|  |  |  |
|  |  |  |
|  |  |  |
|  |  |  |
|  |  |  |
|  |  |  |
|  |  |  |
|  |  |  |
|  |  |  |
|  |  |  |
|  |  |  |
|  |  |  |

| NAME | OCCASION | DATE |
|------|----------|------|
| | | |
| | | |
| | | |
| | | |
| | | |
| | | |
| | | |
| | | |
| | | |
| | | |
| | | |
| | | |
| | | |
| | | |
| | | |
| | | |
| | | |
| | | |
| | | |
| | | |

| NAME | OCCASION | DATE |
|------|----------|------|
| | | |
| | | |
| | | |
| | | |
| | | |
| | | |
| | | |
| | | |
| | | |
| | | |
| | | |
| | | |
| | | |
| | | |
| | | |
| | | |
| | | |
| | | |
| | | |
| | | |

| Name | Occasion | Date |
| --- | --- | --- |
| | | |
| | | |
| | | |
| | | |
| | | |
| | | |
| | | |
| | | |
| | | |
| | | |
| | | |
| | | |
| | | |
| | | |
| | | |
| | | |
| | | |
| | | |
| | | |
| | | |
| | | |

| NAME | OCCASION | DATE |
|------|----------|------|
| | | |
| | | |
| | | |
| | | |
| | | |
| | | |
| | | |
| | | |
| | | |
| | | |
| | | |
| | | |
| | | |
| | | |
| | | |
| | | |
| | | |
| | | |
| | | |
| | | |

| NAME | OCCASION | DATE |
|------|----------|------|
| | | |
| | | |
| | | |
| | | |
| | | |
| | | |
| | | |
| | | |
| | | |
| | | |
| | | |
| | | |
| | | |
| | | |
| | | |
| | | |
| | | |
| | | |
| | | |
| | | |
| | | |
| | | |
| | | |
| | | |

| NAME | OCCASION | DATE |
|------|----------|------|
| | | |
| | | |
| | | |
| | | |
| | | |
| | | |
| | | |
| | | |
| | | |
| | | |
| | | |
| | | |
| | | |
| | | |
| | | |
| | | |
| | | |
| | | |
| | | |
| | | |